D1320765

THE OTHER SIDE
OF THE MOON

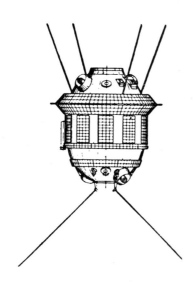

THE OTHER SIDE

OF THE

MOON

Translated from the Russian
by J. B. SYKES

ISSUED BY THE U.S.S.R. ACADEMY OF SCIENCES

PUBLISHED BY

PERGAMON PRESS

OXFORD · LONDON · NEW YORK · PARIS

1960

0074344
523.3

PERGAMON PRESS LTD.
Headington Hill Hall, Oxford
4 & 5 Fitzroy Square, London W.1

PERGAMON PRESS INC.
122 East 55th Street, New York 22, N.Y.
P.O. Box 47715, Los Angeles, California

PERGAMON PRESS S.A.R.L.
24 Rue des Ecoles, Paris Ve

PERGAMON PRESS G.m.b.H.
Kaiserstrasse 75, Frankfurt-am-Main

© 1960 Pergamon Press Ltd.

Library of Congress Card Number 60-9936

PRINTED IN GREAT BRITAIN IN THE CITY OF OXFORD AT THE ALDEN PRESS

SUBJECT SPECIALISATION

V 8348180

523.3

SOMERSET
COUNTY
LIBRARY

HJ

CONTENTS

Foreword

THE DIRECT experimental investigation of the cosmos continues. On 4 October 1959, the Soviet Union successfully launched the third space rocket, the purpose of which was to resolve certain problems in the study of outer space, and to obtain photographs of the other side of the Moon and of its marginal regions. In exact agreement with calculation, the automatic interplanetary station, which had been specially constructed to photograph the other side of the Moon, passed round the Moon and, according to a prearranged programme, photographed the side of the Moon invisible from the Earth. By means of television apparatus the pictures of the Moon were transmitted from the interplanetary station, at a command from the Earth, over a distance of some three hundred thousand miles.

A new era has opened in the history of astronomy. The possibility has been demonstrated, not only of examining the physical properties of outer space and of the various radiations from the heavenly bodies without the difficulties unavoidable in observations from the Earth's surface, but also of obtaining photographs of the planets at close range. No longer will astronomers need to wait some fifteen years for one of the favourable oppositions of Mars, when its distance from the Earth is less than forty million miles. It is now possible, in principle, to send apparatus to the planets to photograph their surfaces.

Man is no longer fettered to the Earth. Soviet citizens have made interplanetary flight a thing of our time.

At the Third Session of the Supreme Soviet of the U.S.S.R., N. S. Khrushchev spoke from the rostrum concerning this unparalleled achievement of Soviet science: 'We are indeed both glad and proud of these Soviet achievements, the successful launching in one year, 1959, of three space rockets, which have earned the admiration of all mankind. The whole Soviet nation applauds the scientists and workers who have paved the way to the cosmos.'

Since the time of Galileo and Newton, the founders of modern science, many notable successes have been won. Among these are the prediction and discovery of Neptune and Pluto, new planets of the solar system. But only in our own day, by the efforts of Soviet citizens, have the first artificial satellites of the Earth and Sun been placed in the heavens, the first flight in history from one body to another been accomplished, the first notable investigations of outer space been conducted. Already the launching of the first Soviet satellites and space rockets has brought to science discoveries of universal importance. The outer belt of radiation and the ring of current around the Earth outside the ionosphere have been revealed; a living creature has made a flight in outer space; new information has been obtained concerning the structure of the Earth's magnetic field; the Moon has been found to have no significant magnetic field or belts of radiation; the density of the interplanetary gas has been determined; and the first photographs of the other side of the Moon have been received.

In this book, the U.S.S.R. Academy of Sciences presents for the first time the results of a preliminary study of those photographs which were made from the automatic interplanetary station. The study of this material continues, and the Academy will shortly issue a scientific publication including the photographs, a description of the features on the opposite side of the Moon, the method of determining their nature, and other information.

The scientists of the Soviet Union hope that the publication of this work on the first photographs of the other side of the Moon will aid the onward advance of science to the conquest of the Universe.

A. N. NESMEYANOV
*Academician and President
of the U.S.S.R. Academy of Sciences*

Introduction

On 4 October 1959 the third space rocket was successfully launched in the Soviet Union. Its purpose was to resolve certain problems in the study of outer space, and the most important of these was to obtain photographs of the surface of the Moon. In particular, it was intended to photograph the part of the Moon's surface which, in consequence of the Moon's motion, cannot be observed from the Earth, and also the part which, being visible only very obliquely, could not otherwise be properly studied.

An automatic interplanetary station was constructed for detailed investigation of outer space and to obtain photographs of the Moon. By means of a multi-stage rocket, the station was placed in an orbit passing round the Moon. In agreement with calculation, the station passed at a distance of a few thousand miles from the Moon and, on account of the Moon's attraction, changed its direction of motion. This made possible a flight path suitable both for photographing the side of the Moon invisible from the Earth and for transmitting scientific data to the Earth.

The launching of the third space rocket and the placing of the automatic interplanetary station in the desired orbit involved the solution of several new problems of science and engineering. The station was launched by means of a powerful multi-stage rocket of improved design, equipped with powerful motors using high-calorie fuel. The motion of the rocket up to the end of its initial trajectory, when the station was released, was adjusted by means of a precise control system.

The scientific investigations carried out by means of the automatic interplanetary station have yielded a considerable quantity of data, which are at present being examined. Photographs have been obtained of the side of the Moon which is invisible from the Earth.

The Design of the Automatic Interplanetary Station

THE AUTOMATIC interplanetary station is a cosmic projectile equipped with a complex array of radio, electronic, photographic, television and other scientific apparatus, a special orientation system, devices for the programmed operation of this apparatus, an automatic system to control the temperature inside the station, and power supplies.

By means of the radio and electronic apparatus in the station, its orbital parameters were measured, television and telemetric data were transmitted to the Earth, and the apparatus control orders were sent from the Earth.

The photographic and television apparatus in the station was used to photograph the other side of the Moon, to develop the film, and to prepare it for transmitting the picture back to the Earth.

The scientific apparatus in the station was designed to investigate further the neighbourhood of the Moon and outer space, continuing the work of the first two Soviet space rockets.

The operation of the apparatus was entirely controlled from the Earth's surface by a radio link, together with programme units in the station. This combined control system makes it possible to carry out scientific experiments most easily and to obtain information from any part of the orbit accessible by radio from the terrestrial observation posts.

A continuously operating automatic temperature control system maintains

11

Fig. I. THE AUTOMATIC INTERPLANETARY STATION,
PHOTOGRAPHED ON ITS MOVABLE CARRIAGE.

12

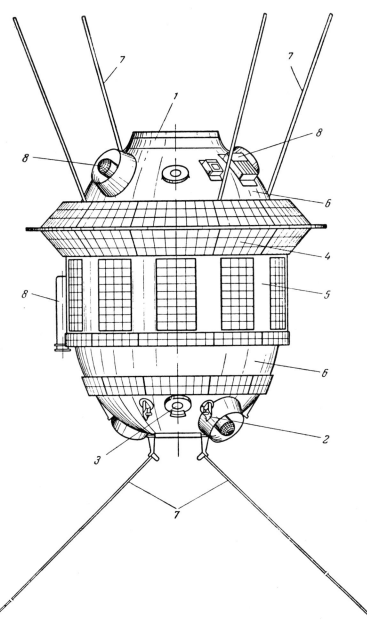

Fig. 2. DIAGRAM SHOWING THE GENERAL APPEARANCE OF THE AUTOMATIC INTERPLANETARY STATION.

1: illuminator for photographic apparatus
2: orientation system motor
3: solar orientation unit
4: solar battery units
5: heat control screens
6: heat shields
7: aerials
8: scientific apparatus

a given temperature distribution within the station, and the heat generated by the apparatus is released into the surrounding space through the radiating surface. For this purpose screens are fitted to the outside of the station, which expose the radiating surface when the temperature inside reaches $+25°$ C.

The power supply system comprises individual chemical sources of current, which supply the apparatus operating during short periods, and a central chemical battery supply. The energy supplied by this battery is replenished by solar batteries. Transformers and stabilizers are used to convey power to the scientific apparatus.

The automatic interplanetary station is a thin sealed shell, cylindrical with spherical ends, within which the apparatus and power supplies are housed. Outside are placed some of the scientific equipment, the radio aerials and the solar battery units. The upper end carries an illuminator with a cover which is automatically removed before photography begins. Beneath the illuminator are the photographic objectives and the lunar orientation devices. Both ends of the station carry small illuminators for the solar units of the orientation system. The lower end carries the motors which control this system of apparatus.

The greatest diameter of the station is about 4 feet, and its length, without the aerials, slightly more than 4 feet.

The most suitable method of photographing the Moon was considered to be that in which the photographic equipment is directed by rotating the entire station. The orientation system was set in rotation and maintained the station in the correct position.

The orientation system was put into operation on approaching the Moon, at a time when the station was approximately on the line joining the Moon and the Sun. The Earth was not on this line. In accordance with calculation, the distance from the Moon, at the time when the orientation system was set in operation, was about 40,000 miles. This position of the station was achieved by appropriate choice of its path, and enabled the station to be oriented on the Moon at a time when it was illuminated by three bright objects, the Sun, the Moon and the Earth.

On coming into operation, the orientation system, which included optical, gyroscopic and electronic-computer apparatus and motors, first stopped the random rotation of the station about its centre of gravity which had been caused by its release from the last stage of the carrier rocket. The lower end of the station was then directed towards the Sun by means of the solar orientation units. In this position the optical axes of the photographic apparatus were directed towards the Moon. An optical unit, whose field of view did not then include the Earth or the Sun, switched off the solar orientation units and directed the photographic apparatus exactly at the Moon. The 'Moon in' signal from this optical unit triggered the automatic photographic process. During the whole of this process, the orientation system ensured that the station remained directed towards the Moon. When all the films had been exposed, the orientation system was switched off, and the station was given a rotation, with the angular velocity chosen so as to improve the thermal conditions but also to avoid any effect of the rotation on the functioning of the scientific apparatus.

The Orbit of the
Interplanetary Station

THE PROBLEMS of orientation and radio communication impose certain conditions on the path of the automatic interplanetary station.

A prerequisite for the correct operation of the orientation system is, as has been mentioned previously, that the Moon, the station and the Sun should be almost in a straight line at the time when the orientation system begins to function, and the station must be at the distance stated in the preceding section.

On account of the great quantity of information to be transmitted from the station to the Earth, the orbit must make it possible for the terrestrial receiving points, which are situated in the U.S.S.R., to obtain the maximum amount of information during the first revolution of the station, and especially when it passes close to the Earth.

It was also most desirable for scientific purposes to have an orbit such that the station would remain in space for some considerable time.

Investigation showed that these requirements can be most completely met by using the Moon's attraction to modify the orbit of the station. If the orbit is to have the desired properties, the Moon's action must be entirely determinate in both magnitude and direction. A considerable effect of the Moon's attraction on the motion of the station can occur only if this attraction is large, and so the station must pass close to the Moon. For a specified change in the orbit, it must pass close to a specified part of the Moon. More precisely, the direction of the Moon's action is determined by the angle between the orbital plane of the station and the plane of the Moon's orbit in the selenocentric motion.

To pass round the Moon and return to the Earth, the station must have, at the end of its initial trajectory, a velocity somewhat less than the parabolic velocity, which is 7 miles per second at the surface of the Earth. The passage round the Moon may then occur along orbits of various kinds.

If the path passes at a distance of a few tens of thousands of miles from the Moon, the effect of the Moon on the orbit is quite small, and the path relative to the Earth is almost an ellipse with one focus at the Earth's centre. Such a path has a number of important disadvantages. It does not make possible a direct investigation of the immediate neighbourhood of the Moon. When the rocket is launched from the northern hemisphere of the Earth, the return flight is towards the southern hemisphere, which hampers observations and the receiving of data at points in the northern hemisphere. The path near the Earth at this time is outside the range of visibility from the northern hemisphere, and radio communication is impossible. On returning to the Earth, the projectile enters the denser layers of the atmosphere and is burnt up, so that the flight ceases after one revolution.

By making use of the directional effect of the Moon's attraction at a close passage to modify the orbit of the automatic interplanetary station, it has been possible to achieve an orbit which does not suffer from these disadvantages.

The orbit of the station passed at a distance of 4900 miles from the Moon's centre, and was so calculated that the station was south of the Moon at the point of closest approach. On account of the Moon's attraction, the path of the station was deflected northwards, as intended. The deflection was so great that the return flight was towards the northern hemisphere of the Earth. After passing the Moon, the station was visible from observation points in the northern hemisphere at maximum altitudes which increased daily. The intervals during which direct communication was possible increased correspondingly. As it approached the Earth, the station remained continuously above the horizon in the northern hemisphere.

On its first return to the Earth, the station did not enter the atmosphere and so was not burnt up; instead, it passed at a distance of 30,000 miles from the Earth's centre, moving in an elongated and almost elliptical orbit. Its greatest distance from the Earth was 300,000 miles.

The path of the station near the Earth did not pass close enough to the surface for the resistance of the atmosphere to exercise any retarding effect. If the motion had continued under the attraction of the Earth alone, therefore, the station would have been a satellite of the Earth and would have remained so indefinitely.

In reality, however, the lifetime of the station is limited. The perturbing effect of the Sun's attraction has the result that the perigee altitude gradually decreases. After a certain number of revolutions the station, returning once more to the Earth, will consequently enter the denser layers of the atmosphere and its existence will terminate.

The decrease in perigee altitude per revolution depends on the size of the orbit and, in particular, on the apogee altitude, with which it increases rapidly. In selecting the path of the station, therefore, it was necessary to make the apogee altitude as small as possible, and not much greater than the distance from the Earth to the Moon. It was also necessary to make the perigee altitude on the first revolution as large as possible. The total number of revolutions of the station round the Earth, and its lifetime, depend on the extent to which these conditions are met.

The action of the Moon is not restricted to that which it exercises during the first approach. The perturbations of the orbit resulting from the Moon's attraction are not so regular as those due to the Sun, and depend greatly on the period of revolution of the station round the Earth. The effect of the Moon may be important if the station again passes fairly close to it on a subsequent revolution. In this case the approach occurs at about the same point in the Moon's orbit as previously, and the nature of the path of the station may be considerably changed. If the station passes south of the Moon, so that the approach is of the same kind as before, the number of revolutions and the lifetime of the station will be considerably increased, although it continues to approach the Earth in the northern hemisphere. If, however, the station passes north of the Moon, the perigee altitude decreases and, if the perturbation is sufficiently great, the station may strike the Earth on its next return.

During revolutions in which there is no close approach to the Moon, the latter nevertheless exerts some action on the path of the station. Although the Moon's attraction is then very small, by acting on a large number of revolutions it perceptibly affects the orbit, reducing the perigee altitude and the lifetime of the station.

The motion of the automatic interplanetary station due to the combined attractions of the Earth, Moon and Sun is very complex. The nature of the

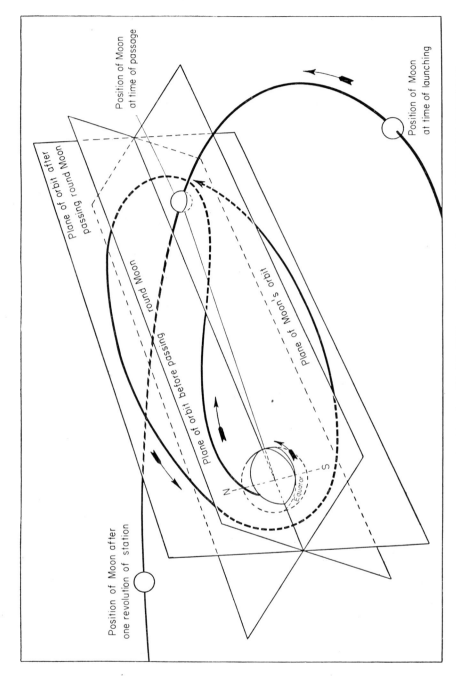

Position of Moon at time of passage

Plane of orbit after passing round Moon

Plane of orbit before passing round Moon

Plane of Moon's orbit

N

S

Equator

Position of Moon after one revolution of station

Position of Moon at time of launching

Fig. 3. DIAGRAM SHOWING THE ORBIT OF THE AUTOMATIC INTERPLANETARY STATION.

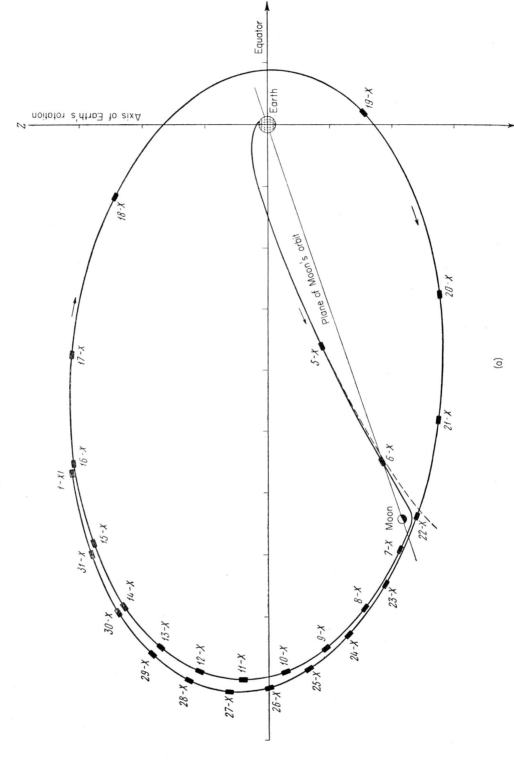

Fig. 4. PATH OF THE AUTOMATIC INTERPLANETARY STATION.

(a) as seen from the vernal equinox
(b) as projected on plane of Earth's equator

(a)

20

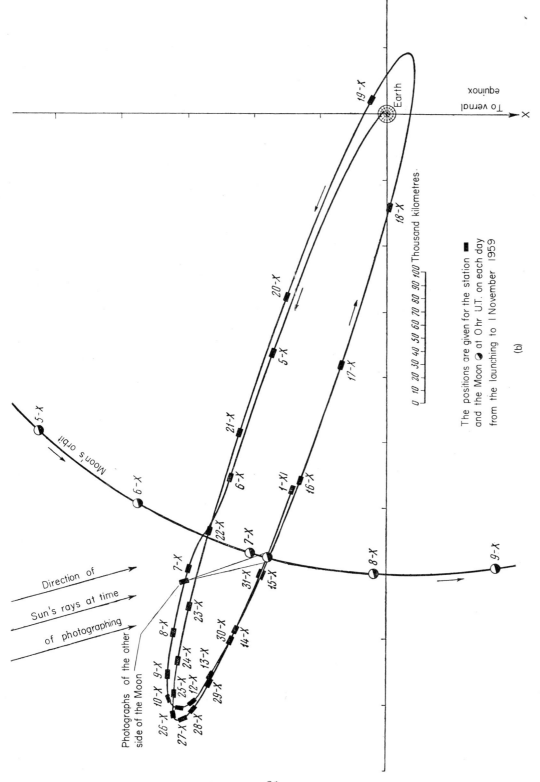

X-19

Earth

To vernal equinox

X-18

X-20

X-5

X-17

X-21

X-6

XI-1

X-16

X-22

X-7

X-31

X-15

X-7

X-8

X-23

X-8

X-24

X-30

X-13

X-14

X-9

X-10

X-9

X-25

X-12

X-29

X-26

X-27

X-28

Moon's orbit

X-5

X-6

X-7

X-8

X-9

Direction of

Sun's rays at time

of photographing

Photographs of the other
side of the Moon

0 10 20 30 40 50 60 70 80 90 100 Thousand kilometres.

The positions are given for the station ■
and the Moon ◖ at 0 hr U.T. on each day
from the launching to 1 November 1959

(b)

21

first passage near the Moon determines the subsequent motion of the station.

Since the orbital motion of the station is not subject to correction, and its entire path is determined by its motion when it is released at the end of the initial trajectory (mainly by the direction and magnitude of its velocity at that time), it is evident that the above-described path of the station can be brought about only by an extremely accurate control of the carrier rocket over the initial trajectory.

If a plane, which may be called the diagram plane, is drawn through the centre of the Moon perpendicular to the line joining the Earth and the Moon, the nature of the orbit relative to the Moon can be defined by the position of the point at which it intersects this plane. Calculation shows that, when the point of intersection is six hundred miles from its intended position, the minimum distance of the station from the Earth after one revolution may change by from three to six thousand miles, and the time of its return by from 10 to 14 hours.

Although the fulfilment of the conditions imposed on the orbit permits greater deviations from the calculated position of the point of intersection with the diagram plane than were possible in launching a projectile to strike the Moon, as was done with the second Soviet space rocket, the requirements of accuracy in the initial trajectory remain equally rigorous. This is largely due to the fact that errors in the magnitude of the velocity at the end of this trajectory for an elliptical orbit cause deviations in the point where the orbit intersects the diagram plane which are three to four times those for the hyperbolic orbits which were suitable for an impact projectile.

The perturbing effect of the Moon at a close approach considerably increases the effect of the difference between the actual and intended motion at the end of the initial trajectory on the nature of the motion when the station returns to the Earth after passing round the Moon. Hence even slight errors of this kind will lead to very great errors in calculating the motion on the return flight.

In addition, in order to achieve reliable radio communication between the interplanetary station and the observing points on the Earth, the time variation of its motion must be quite accurately known. This is necessary in order to calculate with sufficient accuracy the position to which the observations should be directed and the times at which the transmitting apparatus in the station should be caused to operate. The path of the station must therefore be continually observed, the results examined and the orbit more precisely defined, both before and after reaching the Moon. The effect of the Sun and

Moon on the orbit of the station as it continues its motion also demands continual measurement and correction of the values of the orbital parameters.

These conditions impose stringent requirements on the operation of the apparatus on the Earth whose function is to measure the orbital parameters of the station, predict its motion, calculate the directions for measurement and observation, and calculate the time when the transmitting apparatus should be used as the station passes near the Earth. This apparatus includes radio observing stations for measuring distance, angle and radial velocity, stations for receiving telemetric information, and automatic communication lines between the measuring points and a co-ordinating and computing centre, which in turn is connected to the stations on the Earth which send out the orders for the operation of the transmitting apparatus in the interplanetary station.

Such a radio link makes possible the operation of the radio communications at particular times when the conditions are favourable for a transmission between the apparatus in the station and the ground observing points in the Soviet Union. The time of commencement and the duration of radio communication are determined by the operating conditions of the apparatus in the station, by the necessity of making measurements of the orbit to improve predictions of its motion, and by the power supply conditions in the station.

The information concerning the positions of the interplanetary station at the times when the first and last photographs were taken was obtained from orbit measurements, and is necessary for the purpose of identifying the position of objects on the hitherto invisible side of the Moon with respect to a selenographic co-ordinate system. The results are shown in the following table.

	Date	Time (U.T.)	Distance from Moon's centre (miles)
Beginning	1959 October 7	$3^h 30^m$	40750
End	1959 October 7	$4^h 10^m$	42750

	Selenographic co-ordinates of station	
	Latitude	Longitude
Beginning	16°·9	117°·6
End	17°·3	117°·1

A preliminary reduction of the orbit measurements for the first revolution has shown that the station will remain in its orbit until the end of March 1960, completing eleven revolutions round the Earth.

Photography and Image Transmission

THE DESIGN of the equipment for photographing the other side of the Moon and transmitting the results back to the Earth from the automatic interplanetary station involved setting up a photographic and television system giving sufficiently clear half-tone images which could be transmitted over distances of hundreds of thousands of miles.

The photographic and television apparatus in the station comprised the following principal components: a photographic system with two objectives, a miniature developing and fixing unit, a miniature cathode-ray tube, a high-stability photomultiplier, electronic circuitry including amplifiers and sweep generators, and the automatic control and programming equipment.

The apparatus was designed so as to be capable of operating during the flight of the station in outer space. For this purpose the photographic materials had to be protected from the effects of cosmic radiation, and the film treatment unit and other components had to function properly under conditions of weightlessness.

In order to effect the very long-range transmission of the pictures with a radio transmitter of very low power, the rate of transmission was some tens of thousands of times slower than that of ordinary television stations.

For the first photographs of the other side of the Moon it was desirable to include as large as possible a part of the hitherto unseen surface. Thus it was

24

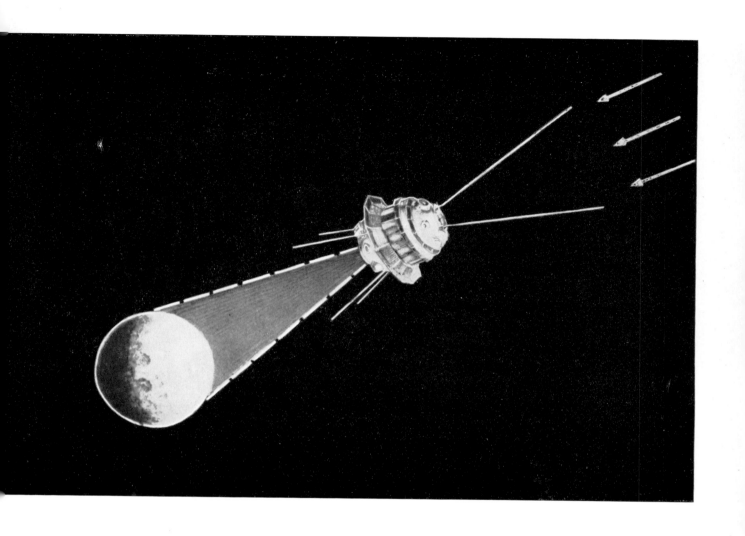

Fig. 5. POSITION OF THE AUTOMATIC INTERPLANETARY STATION IN SPACE WHEN PHOTOGRAPHING THE OTHER SIDE OF THE MOON.

The arrows show the direction of the Sun's rays.

necessary to photograph the fully illuminated disc, for which the contrast is always much smaller than under oblique illumination, which throws shadows. In order to improve the transmission of the low-contrast picture, an automatic image-contrast control was used in the apparatus.

The photographic system contained two objectives of focal lengths 8 and 20 inches, operating at $f/5\cdot6$ and $f/9\cdot5$ respectively. The former gave an image of the Moon's disc which was small enough for the photograph to include the whole of it. The other objective gave a larger-scale image of a part of the disc. The photographs were taken on special 35-millimetre film which was suitable for treatment at a high temperature.

The exposure was automatically varied so as to obtain negatives of the correct density, and the total time occupied by the photography was about 40 minutes, during which numerous photographs of the other side of the Moon were taken.

The whole of the photographic and development process was carried out automatically according to a specified programme.

To prevent fogging of the film by cosmic radiation, special protection was designed on the basis of results obtained with Soviet satellites and space rockets. After the exposure, the film entered the miniature treatment unit, where it was developed, dried and fixed. It then passed to another container for preparation for transmission of the pictures.

The pictures of the Moon were transmitted in response to orders from the Earth, whereby the television apparatus power supply in the interplanetary station was switched on, the film was placed in position, and the television apparatus was connected to the transmitters. An automatic programmed control system ensured the correct operation of the whole apparatus, including electronic, optical, mechanical and chemical units.

In order to convert the image on the negative film into electrical signals, a scanning method was employed, similar to that used in the ordinary television transmission of cinematograph films: a miniature cathode-ray tube of high resolving power produced a bright spot which was projected on the film by means of an optical system. The light transmitted by the film operated a photomultiplier which converted the light signal into an electrical one. The bright spot on the cathode-ray tube screen moved in accordance with electrical signals generated by a sweep circuit. The image of the bright spot on the film moved uniformly across the film from one side to the other and then returned rapidly to its original position to resume its uniform motion. This gave a line sweep of the image. The film itself was moved slowly past the cathode-ray tube so as to give a frame sweep.

The intensity of the light coming from the cathode-ray tube through the film to the photomultiplier depends on the density of the negative at the point where the bright spot is situated. As the spot moves over the negative, the current in the photomultiplier varies in a similar manner to the image density along the path of the spot. Thus the output signal from the photomultiplier gave an image signal which reproduced the variation in the density of the negative along the path.

The image signals were amplified and shaped by a specially designed stabilized narrow-band amplifier.

Since the mean density of the negative and the image contrast could not be accurately foreseen, the amplifier included an automatic control unit to compensate the effect of variations in the mean density on the output signal, and an automatic control of the tube brightness was provided to compensate changes in contrast.

The film had already received test marks, some of which were developed on the Earth before launching, and others in the interplanetary station during the treatment of the film after the pictures of the other side of the Moon had been taken. These marks were transmitted to the Earth in order to check the processes of photography, film treatment and picture transmission.

Two rates of image transmission were provided for: a slower transmission at great distances, and a faster transmission on approaching the Earth. The number of lines in the image was variable and depended on the rate of transmission, the maximum number being 1000 per frame.

To synchronize the transmitting and receiving sweeps, a method was used which gave good stability against interference and was reliable in operation.

The radio link was such that signals could be sent in either direction. The order signals controlling the operation of the apparatus were sent from the Earth to the interplanetary station, and the television signals, scientific apparatus readings and orbit measurements were sent in the opposite direction. The ground equipment included powerful radio transmitters, high-sensitivity receivers, recording apparatus, and receiving and transmitting aerials. The radio equipment in the interplanetary station included transmitters, receivers, aerials and apparatus for dealing with orders and programmes.

The pictures of the Moon were sent from the station by means of the same radio link as was used to measure the orbital parameters. This transmission and all other operations of radio communication from the station were effected by continuous (not pulsed) emission of radio waves. The combination of operations in a single radio link with continuous emission was here achieved for the first time, and ensured good radio communications up to the greatest distances concerned, while keeping the energy consumption in the station to a minimum.

All the radio apparatus, both in the station and on the Earth, was duplicated to increase the reliability of the communication system. If one of the pieces of radio equipment in the station broke down or ceased to operate, it could be replaced by the reserve equipment by means of the appropriate order from the ground control point.

The amount of scientific information transmitted by radio, including the pictures of the Moon, greatly exceeded that which was sent by the first two Soviet space rockets. In consequence, methods of high efficiency, involving the minimum consumption of energy from the power supplies in the station, had to be used in taking the photographs and transmitting the signals by radio.

Semiconductors, ferrites and other modern equipment were used in the radio and electronic apparatus of the station. Particular attention was paid to minimizing the size and weight of the apparatus, so that the weight and size of the power supply units could be increased. For reasons of economy of electrical energy, the power of the radio transmitters in the station was set at a few watts.

The difficulties of ensuring reliable radio communication with the inter-planetary station are shown by a calculation of the fraction of the power emitted by its radio transmitters which reaches the receiving apparatus on the Earth. In order to maintain communication with the station as it rotates, the aerials must emit radio signals in all directions equally, and so the power received per unit area is about the same at any point on a sphere whose centre is at the position of the station. The fraction of the emitted power which is received by an aerial on the Earth is given by the ratio of the effective area of the receiving aerial to the surface area of a sphere whose radius is equal to the distance of this aerial from the station. Large receiving aerials were used in order to increase the effective receiving area. Yet the fraction of the power emitted by the station transmitter which was received, when the station was at its greatest distance from the Earth, was a hundred million times less than the average power received by an ordinary television receiver. Such weak signals can be detected only by very sensitive receiving equipment with a low internal noise level.

The internal noise at the output of the ground receiving equipment was minimized by various means. According to information theory and the theory of stability against interference, very weak signals against a background of noise can be detected by reducing the rate of transmission of information. The extent of this reduction depends on the method of transmitting and receiving the signals.

The processing and transmission of radio signals, both in the station and on the Earth, were such as to reduce the noise level as much as possible, while maintaining an acceptable rate of transmission.

The economical use of the power supplies in the station, the setting up of radio communication with continuous emission and combination of functions, and the use on the Earth of special receiving aerials, high-sensitivity receiving equipment, and special methods of signal processing and transmission, jointly made possible a reliable radio link with the automatic interplanetary station, the trouble-free operation of the order signal system, and the obtaining of pictures of the Moon and telemetric data according to plan.

The pictures of the Moon were received by means of special television image equipment which recorded the signals on film, magnetic tape recorders with highly stabilized tape speed, skiatrons (cathode-ray tubes in which the image remains on the screen for some time), and direct recording apparatus in which the image was developed on electrochemical paper. Materials recorded in all these ways were used in the study of the other side of the Moon.

By means of the radio and television equipment in the automatic interplanetary station, the images were transmitted over distances of up to 290,000 miles. This confirmed that it is possible to transmit half-tone pictures through space over very large distances with high clarity and without marked distortion during the propagation of the radio waves.

The Unseen Side of the Moon

THE PERIOD of the Moon's rotation about its axis is the same as that of its revolution round the Earth, and so the Moon always turns the same side to the Earth. In the far distant past, many millions of years ago, the Moon rotated more rapidly than it now does, completing a rotation in a few hours. The forces of tidal friction exerted by the Sun and the Earth have slowed down the Moon's rotation, the period of which is now 27·32 days.

For 350 years telescopic observations have been used to map the side of the Moon which is visible from the Earth. From the first sketches of the lunar surface, such maps have been gradually improved and completed as observational equipment and methods were perfected. At the present time there are maps which show tens of thousands of the ring-shaped mountains called craters, many mountain ranges, dark regions of the Moon called *maria* or seas, strangely shaped fissures, and many other details of the lunar surface.

The existence of librations of the Moon, which are periodic oscillations about its centre with respect to the Earth, have made possible the study and mapping of 59% of the Moon's surface. Some lunar objects lie on the very edge of the visible disc, and are seen only during particular librations. All maps of the marginal regions are subject to distortions resulting from the effect of foreshortening.

The time chosen for the taking of photographs by the automatic interplanetary station made it possible to obtain pictures of the greater part of the region of the Moon not visible from the Earth, together with a small part of the region already known. The disc of the Moon as seen from the station was in almost full sunlight. In such illumination conditions the features of the lunar surface throw no shadows, and some are not easily distinguished. Since the photographs include a part of the Moon's surface that is visible from the Earth, the features on the other side of the Moon, which have never been observed before, can be correlated with the selenographic co-ordinate system by means of their positions with respect to known objects. The boundary between the parts of the Moon which are visible and invisible from the Earth is shown in the photograph (Fig. 8) by a dashed line.

Among the objects photographed from the interplanetary station which are visible from the Earth are Mare Humboldtianum, Mare Crisium, Mare Marginis, Mare Smythii and part of Mare Australe.

These *maria*, which lie at the extreme edge of the part of the Moon visible from the Earth, appear long and narrow on account of the effects of foreshortening, and their true form is now known for the first time. On the photographs taken from the interplanetary station they are no longer at the edge of the Moon's disc, and the distortion is negligible.

From a preliminary study of the photographs now available it is seen that the hitherto invisible part of the Moon's surface is predominantly mountainous, with very few *maria* similar to those on the visible side. There are noticeable crater-like *maria* in the southern and equatorial regions.

Of the *maria* lying near the edge of the region hitherto known, Mare Humboldtianum, Mare Marginis, Mare Smythii and Mare Australe are clearly distinguishable with almost no distortion. It is found that a considerable part of Mare Australe lies on the other side of the Moon, and its boundary is irregular.

Mare Smythii is more rounded than Mare Australe, and south of it lies a mountainous region. A considerable part of this *mare* also is on the unseen side of the Moon. Mare Marginis is elongated, and has an indentation on the side opposite to Mare Crisium. Like Mare Smythii, it extends to the unseen side of the Moon. Mare Humboldtianum has an unusual pear-shaped outline.

The whole of the region near the western edge of the other side of the Moon has a reflecting power intermediate between those of mountains and of *maria*, and similar to that of the region between the craters Tycho and Petavius and Mare Nectaris.

N

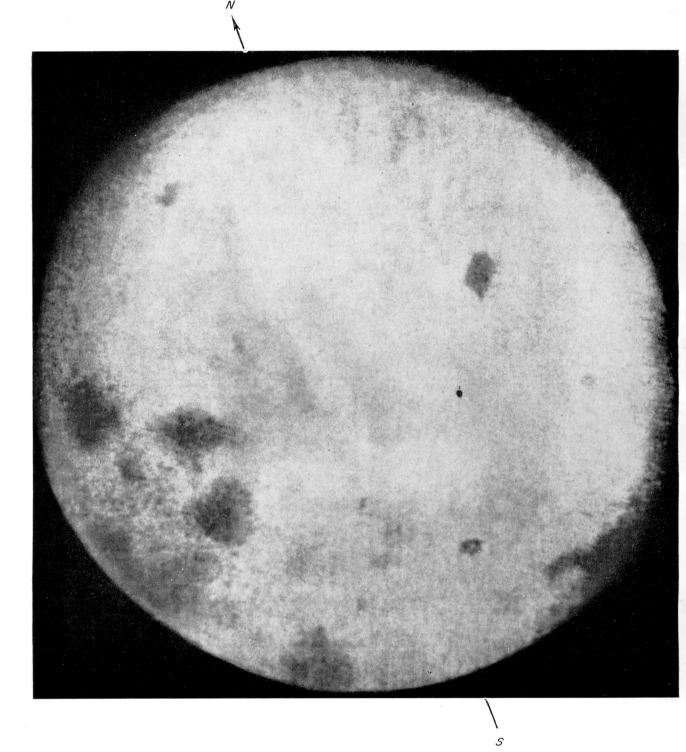

S

Fig. 6. PHOTOGRAPH OF THE OTHER SIDE OF THE MOON
OBTAINED BY THE AUTOMATIC INTERPLANETARY STATION.

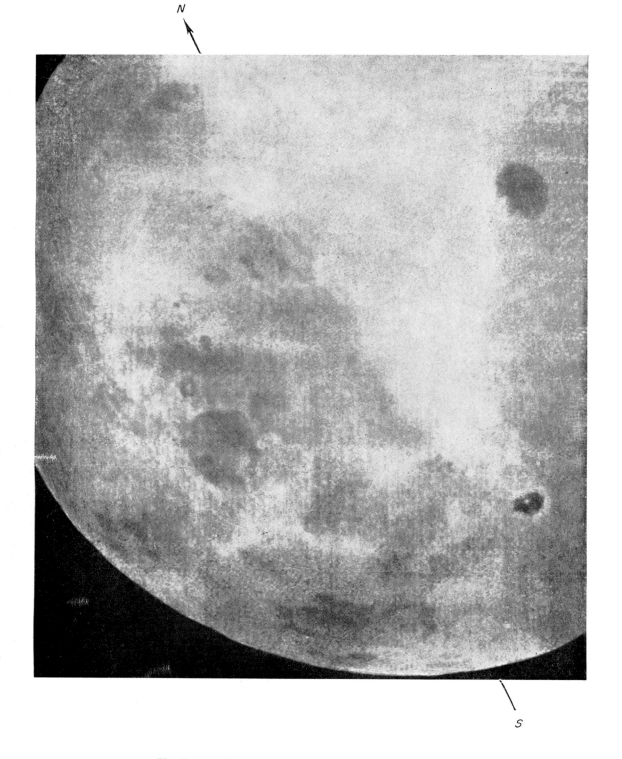

Fig. 7. PHOTOGRAPH OF THE OTHER SIDE OF THE MOON
OBTAINED BY THE AUTOMATIC INTERPLANETARY STATION.

Fig. 8. OBJECTS ON THE SIDE OF THE MOON INVISIBLE FROM THE EARTH, SHOWN BY A PRELIMINARY EXAMINATION OF PHOTOGRAPHS OBTAINED BY THE AUTOMATIC INTERPLANETARY STATION.

1. Mare Moscovianum, a large crater-like *mare* of diameter 200 miles
2. Sinus Astronautarum, a bay of Mare Moscovianum
3. Continuation of Mare Australe on the other side of the Moon
4. Tsiolkovskiĭ, a crater with a central peak
5. Lomonosov, a crater with a central peak
6. Joliot-Curie, a crater
7. Soviet Mountains
8. Mare Somnii

The continuous line across the photograph shows the Moon's equator, the dashed line the boundary between the parts of the Moon visible and invisible from the Earth. Objects whose existence has been reliably established from a preliminary examination are enclosed by a continuous line, those whose shape requires confirmation, by a dashed line, and those whose nature requires clarification, by a dotted line. The examination of the photographic materials continues.

The Roman figures denote objects on the side of the Moon visible from the Earth.

   I: Mare Humboldtianum
  II: Mare Crisium
 III: Mare Marginis, continued on the unseen side
  IV: Mare Undarum
   V: Mare Smythii, continued on the unseen side
  VI: Mare Foecunditatis
 VII: Mare Australe, continued on the unseen side

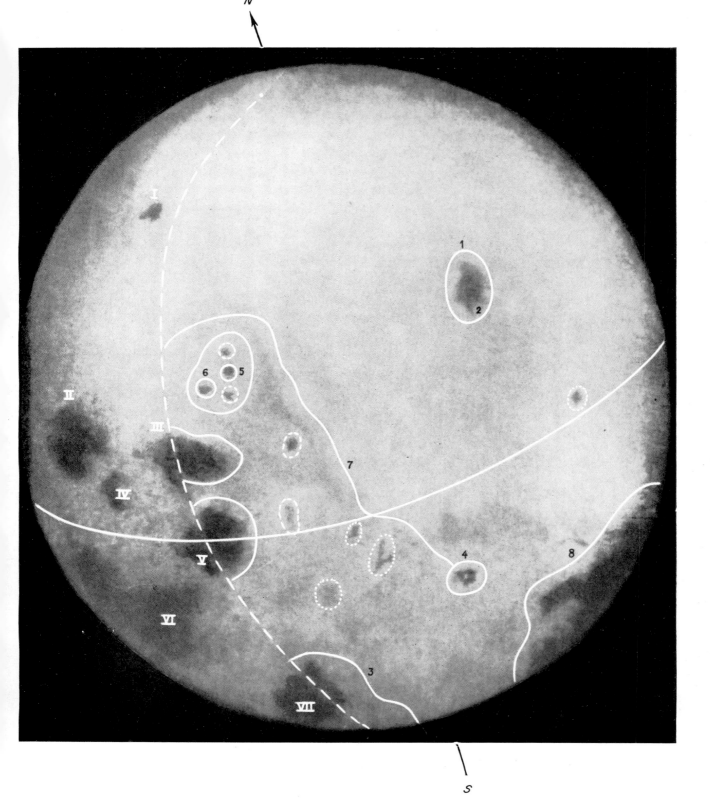

South-south-east of Mare Humboldtianum, at the edge of the region just mentioned, is a chain of mountains whose total length exceeds 1250 miles, crossing the equator and extending into the southern hemisphere. Beyond this there appears to be a region of plains with high reflecting power.

Between latitudes $+20°$ and $+30°$ and longitudes $+140°$ and $+160°$ lies a crater-like *mare* of diameter about 200 miles, terminated to the south by a bay. In the southern hemisphere, at about latitude $-30°$ and longitude $+130°$, is a large crater of diameter over 60 miles, with a dark floor, a bright central peak, and a wide and bright rim.

To the east of the mountain chain already mentioned, at about $+30°$ north latitude, is a group of four medium-sized craters, the largest being about 45 miles in diameter. South-west of this group, at about latitude $+10°$ and longitude $+110°$, lies a single circular crater. In the southern hemisphere, near the western edge, are two regions of markedly low reflecting power.

The photographs also show various regions of slightly higher or lower reflecting power, and many details. The nature, shape and size of these features may be determined when the photographs have been studied more thoroughly.

The first successful television transmission of pictures of the other side of the Moon from the interplanetary station opens new prospects in the study of the planets of the solar system.